? ? ? ? NAGAGRA

See if you can work out the following are all horse or pony breeds.

WEN FSOERT ROOMATRD IAPSACN

IEHSR TQARRUE SERHO BRAA ANNACMORE

SHEWL BOC DANLTESH LADE FLEL

ROXOME GORMNA ERNOPERCH HSIIR HUGTARD

? ? PONY POSERS ? ?

Here are some quick questions, which will be especially useful for anyone who is getting ready to take Pony Club tests. They range from 'D' to 'B' standards.

1 What is the name for a pony who is (a) black and white? (b) golden with a cream mane and tail?
2 What is a snip and where would you find it?
3 What are very young male and female ponies called?
4 Your pony is tied up, ready to be groomed. What do you do first?
5 How many sponges should you keep in your grooming kit, and what are they used for?
6 Before grooming your pony's head, what is the first thing that you should do?
7 Name three types of girth.
8 What is a crupper used for?
9 What protective clothing should you put on your pony to prevent injury when travelling?
10 There are nine rules of good feeding practice. How many can you name?
11 Name three plants which are poisonous to ponies.
12 How do you know when your pony needs shoeing?
13 What can be fitted into the heel of a shoe to lessen the risk of slipping?
14 What is (a) your pony's normal temperature? (b) his normal breathing time at rest? (c) his normal pulse rate?

Answers on page 29

A BIT OF A PUZZLE

Can you name these bits?

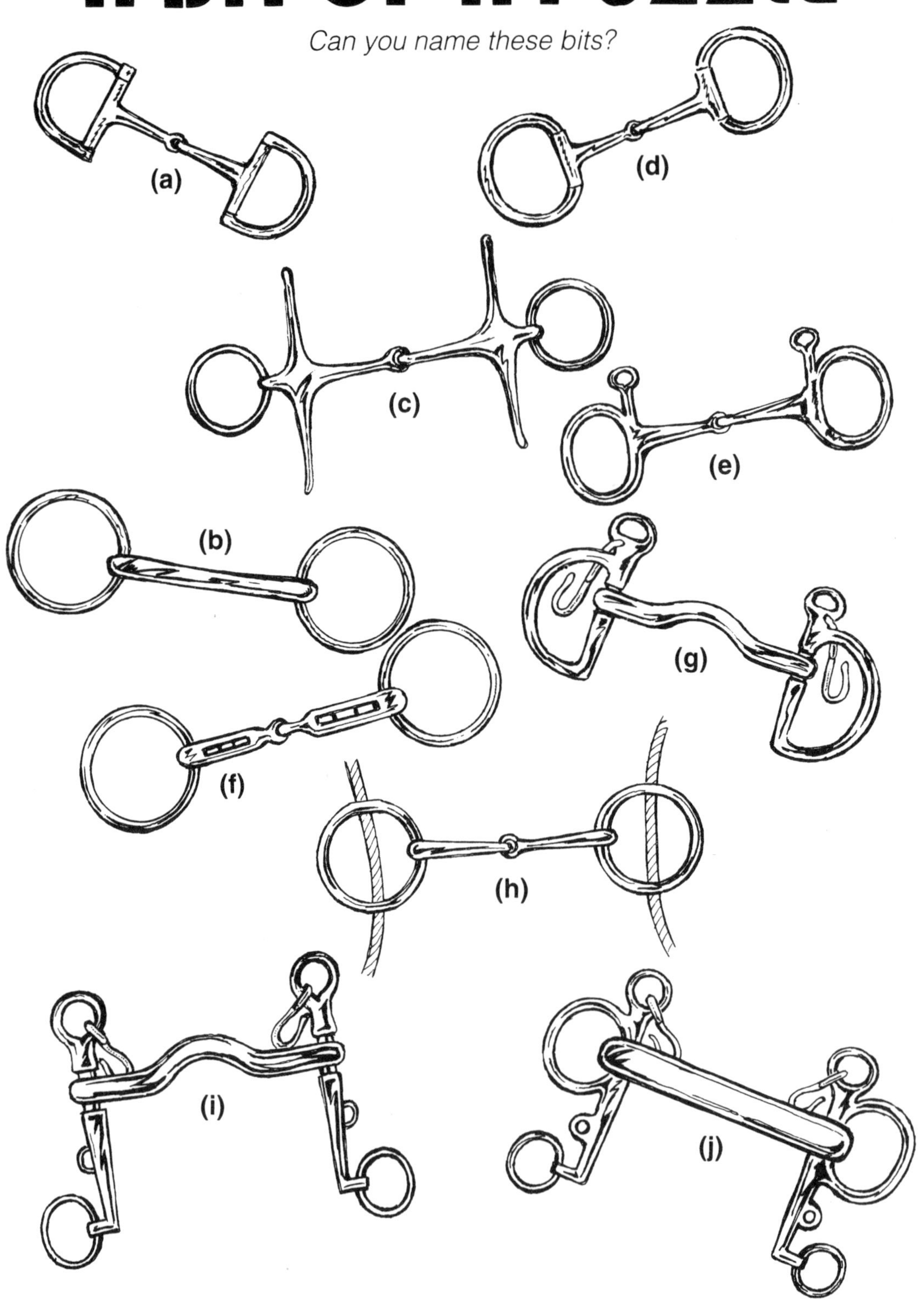

Answers on page 29

Katie-Jane Learns her Lesson

Part One

This is the story of a rather naughty little girl and her pony, Wilbur. See if you can spot the things which you would not allow to happen if you were lucky enough to own a pony. There is a column down the side of the page so that you can mark the incorrect sentences with a cross.

Katie-Jane couldn't wait to go riding. (Sitting in a classroom always seems worse when it is sunny outside.) At last the bell had rung and here she was at home. But what a disappointment. "Sorry K-J.," said Mother. "We just don't have time to go riding today. The washing machine has broken down and I must stay in to wait for the man to come and mend it."

Katie-Jane had other ideas! She was definitely going for a ride, so she slipped out of her uniform and pulled on some riding clothes – a cool pair of shorts and white trainers. Then she ran downstairs, grabbed the bridle from the hook and raced down the path shouting "Hello Wilbur! Cooee!" at the top of her voice.

She climbed carefully over the broken-down wire and old bedsteads which divided Wilbur's paddock from the garden. She could see Wilbur standing under an old yew tree, asleep. So she thought that she would creep up behind him and give him a nice surprise by slapping him on the rump and shouting "Boo!"

Fortunately for Katie-Jane, Wilbur was not really asleep . . . he just *looked* as though he was. All of that shouting in the garden had woken him up. It was so snooze-making in the sun that he hadn't bothered to open his eyes.

Wilbur was a wise old pony. He knew exactly what Katie-Jane had forgotten: it was a little something which most ponies won't be caught without. So he decided to teach Katie-Jane a little lesson. He waited until she had crept to just within kicking distance, then he shot forward like a greyhound from a trap and galloped off, full speed ahead. It was Katie who had the surprise! For ten minutes Wilbur played 'cat and mouse' with his young rider. He seemed to have a magic barrier around his chunky little body. Katie-Jane could get close to him – but not quite close enough to catch him.

Finally Katie-Jane gave up and stalked crossly back across the paddock. Wilbur waited by the old bath which served as a water trough, and when Katie returned with some nuts, he allowed himself to be caught.

Katie-Jane put the headpiece of the bridle over his ears then stood in front and pulled the bit over his nose and nostrils and into his mouth. Next she led him to the back door; she had forgotten to bring out the saddle. But what could she do with Wilbur?

For Part 2, turn to page 22

Answers on page 30

CHARADES

This game will put your acting skills to the test. It is best played with a group of three or more people. One person must mime the clue (no talking is allowed) and the others must guess what the horsey word is.
For example: 'Sharp as a needle without an eye' (Pin) and 'One of the ten things found on your feet' (Toe). Answer: Pinto. *(As this is a miming game you can cheat with the spelling!)*

1 People mop this when they get hot (brow).
A group of musicians (band).
2 A crunchy fruit which keeps the doctor away (apple)
What you need to make something which is too tight (looser)
3 An animal who says "Moo": (cow).
Dogs always manage to do this on your face (lick).
4 Tarzan thumps this part of his body (chest).
A food which has to be cracked before you can eat it (nut).
5 For removing pencil marks (rubber).
Hot Indian food (curry).
How to keep your hair tidy (comb).
6 A little arrow used in a pub game (dart).
You might ask your Mum for this if you were still hungry (more).
7 Four and twenty blackbirds were baked in one (pie).
Without hair (bald).
8 The number which comes after three (four).
What you do with a key (lock).
9 A fierce animal which can stand on its hind legs (bear).
The place on a pony where you put the saddle (back).
10 Not low (high).
What aeroplanes do when they reach an airport (land).
11 The box in which people are buried (coffin).
What a dog likes to chew (bone).
12 What you say to a dog if you want to remain still (stay).
Something which you press to make a ringing noise (bell).

CROSSWORD

ACROSS

1 A shaped blanket which fits under the saddle (6).
4 An excitable pony or the best method of shoeing (3).
5 Clean and fresh, ponies should always have this in their field or stable (5).
7 Name for someone who looks after racehorses (3).
8 A slippery fish or a line down a dun pony's back (3).
9 Boots and ponies' coats do this when well brushed (5).
11 A pony who limps is? (4).
13 Straw makes a comfortable? (3).
14 Old native breed which lives in woodland area (3, 6).
17 Initials used in racing which mean "pulled up" (2).
18 Said to be the key to a horse's mouth (3).
19 Turn it on to get water (3).
20 Pony summering in a paddock is ". . . grass" (2).
21 Definitely not white! (4).
22 Describes a hat worn on very grand occasions (3).

DOWN

1 Waterproof for ponies from 'down under' (3, 7, 3).
2 Buckles, bits and stirrups are all made of this (5).
3 Measure of land (5).
4 A rope headcollar (6).
6 Thinner than a blaze (6).
10 Somewhere to rest your foot (7).
12 To cut grass for hay (3).
15 Good feed for horses, but can make ponies too frisky (4).
16 Growing at the back of the fetlock, it reminds us that prehistoric horse had more than one toe (5).
17 How to reward your pony (3).
19 Clean out the threads in your stud-holes (3).

Answers on page 29 & 32

ACHES AND PAINS

Link the symptom with the ailment

● *SYMPTOMS* ☆ *AILMENTS*

● *The pony has a dry, shallow cough, looks off colour and has lost his appetite. There is a slight discharge from his nose. His eyes, and gums are inflamed and there is a noticeable rise in his temperature.* ***(D)***

● *The pony has been on lush pasture and is very reluctant to walk. He is standing on his heels with his forefeet thrust forward.* ***(A)***

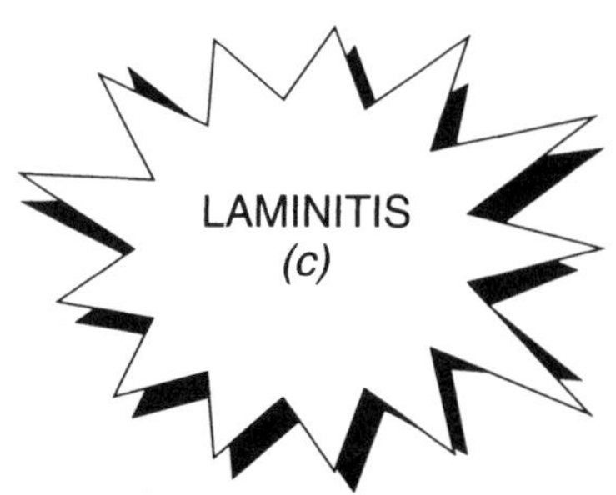

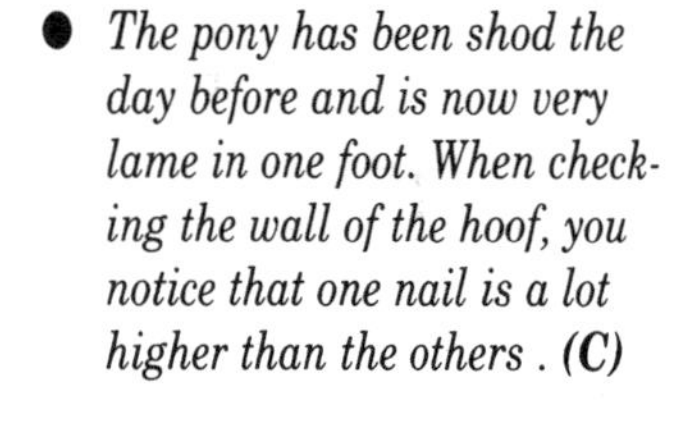

● *The pony is obviously uncomfortable and miserable. He has lost his appetite and keeps looking at and sometimes kicking his belly.* ***(E)***

● *The pony has been shod the day before and is now very lame in one foot. When checking the wall of the hoof, you notice that one nail is a lot higher than the others .* ***(C)***

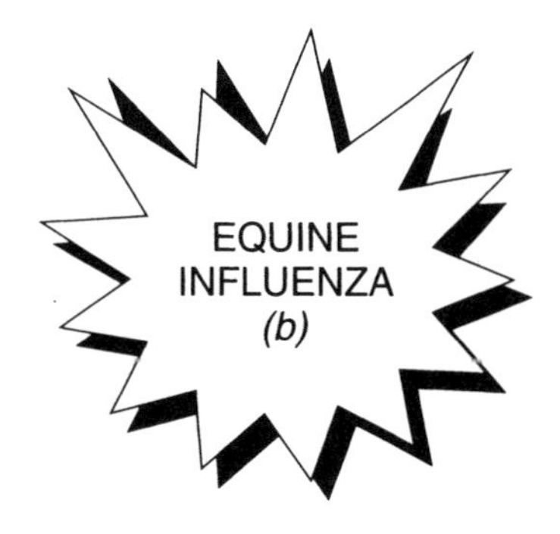

● *The pony is suffering from an itch, especially around the base of his ears, crest and tail. He is rubbing the areas until they are bare and is losing condition. You part the mane and see tiny insects crawling about.* ***(B)***

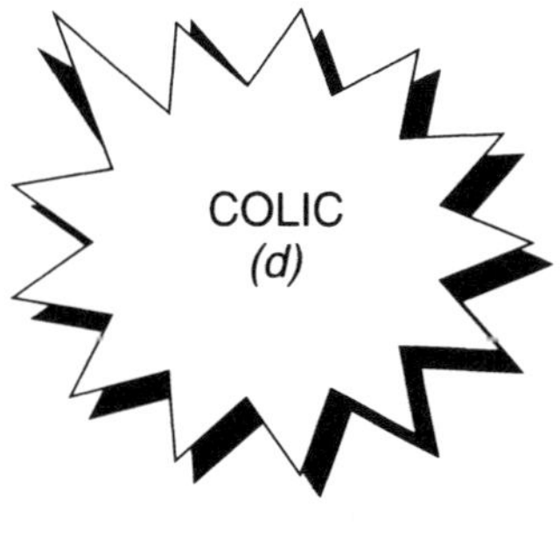

Answers on page 29

DEALER

You are working for Mr Wiley-Coper the local horse dealer who has gone abroad on holiday and has given you a list of the horses in his yard. When customers telephone the yard, you ask for all the necessary details, and write them down. Luckily there are three more horses than customers. See if you can find the horses to suit the buyers.

1 Brainstorm. Striking 17.hh chestnut thoroughbred gelding. 13 years old. He has run over hurdles and is an exciting point-to-point or team chase prospect. Will hunt all day and never stops. Not a novice ride.

2 Iris. Delightful black Warmblood mare with papers. 16.3hh, 6 years old. Superb paces and manners. Through no fault of her own, she has not much competition experience and no points, but is working nicely at dressage elementary level at home. Sold sound.

3 Cuthbert. 14.3hh, skewbald gelding. Aged but still active. Very genuine cob type. Quiet to ride and drive. Excellent confidence giver.

4 Ranger. 16.3hh, 7 years old, bay gelding. An athletic, well-mannered middle/heavyweight, oozing with quality and scope. A safe jumper with a good gallop, he is sold as a genuine, sound, top-class hunter.

5 Primrose. Charming, bright bay 8 year-old mare, 15hh, halfbred New Forest. Easy-going little horse with excellent temperament. Has completed successfully in most Pony Club and Riding Club disciplines. Quiet to box, shoe and on the road. Open to Vet. Sold sound.

6 Hector. Superb Irish Draught gelding. 5 years old, 16hh. Immense power and substance, but with surprising turn of foot and good jump. Has hunted in Ireland. Although still rather green has the makings of being a real gentleman. Sold sound.

7 Golden Sovereign. 16hh chestnut gelding, 7/8th bred by "I'm top of the Tree". 7 years old. Super intermediate

Answers on page 29

S GAME

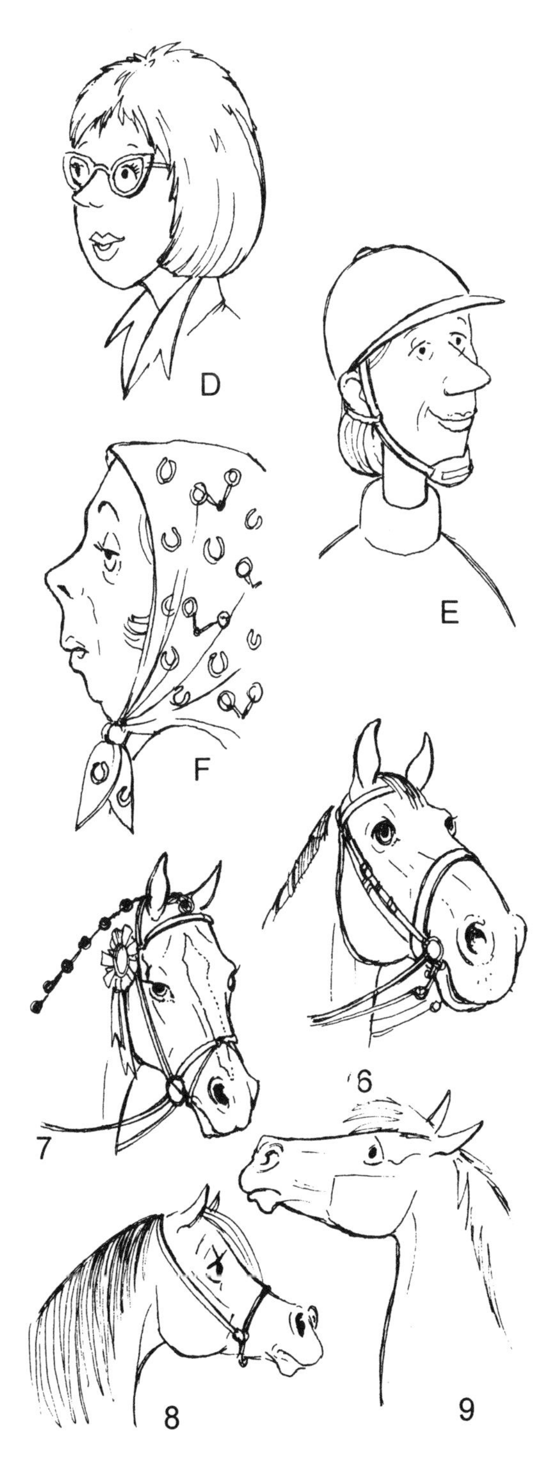

eventer with excellent temperament and ability. Has never stopped or fallen and would be an excellent schoolmaster for a young rider, yet with the scope to build on his already impressive record. Quiet in the stable, to shoe, clip, box and on the road. Sold sound.

8 Zanzibar. Grey Arabian colt, 15hh. Excellent conformation, bloodlines and fantastic action. Has been shown in hand, backed and ridden away. Open to Vet.

9 Cream Cracker. 11-year old palomino Anglo Arab mare. Still a novice but shows potential in all spheres. Nervous in traffic. Crib bites.

A Jerome 'Hotspur' Harkaway is looking for a top quality hunter to hunt with a leading Hunt next season. He weighs 14 stone and wants something with ability and manners to spare.

B Madame Saccharin has taken up dressage. She wants a beautiful horse who is capable of working to a high standard, but she is prepared to bring on a novice. Madame is an ex-model and is 6 feet tall.

C 'Jumbo' Barleymow is a keen hunting farmer with limited time for pampering horses. He is looking for a tough hunter for next season, to go in plough country and capable of carrying 17 stone.

D Miss Willing is a secretary who wants a horse to do weekend Riding Club work. It must live out. As she has no help or transport, the horse must be amenable in every way and good in traffic. Miss Willing is 5 feet 2 inches and weighs 7 stone.

E Ms. Leatherbottom is looking for a young, unspoilt horse. Her sport is long-distance riding and she has a particular fondness for Arabs.

F The Hon Mrs Fortescew-Ffitz-Blogs wants to buy an event horse for her teenage daughter Clarinda. The horse must be sound and experienced – with the potential to go to Badminton.

Answers on page 29

EYE SPY AT THE SHOW

This is a game which you can play with your friends when you are at a show. Agree to a time period, then split up and see if you can see any of the things mentioned below. Try to get as many points as possible.

		points
1	A horse or pony being lunged	5
2	An unshod horse or pony	3
3	A horse or pony wearing an Irish martingale	8
4	A horse being unloaded or loaded up wearing a poll guard	10
5	A lady riding side-saddle	8
6	A Fjord pony	10
7	A horse wearing tendon boots	1
8	Someone putting in studs	5
9	A mare and foal	6
10	A loose horse	5
11	A horse or pony wearing a three-fold girth	9
12	An iron grey pony	2
13	Someone watering their horse or pony	5
14	A horse or pony with a hogged mane	10
15	A Shire horse	5
16	A pony with an eel strip	8
17	A horse or pony wearing a neckstrap	9
18	A bay pony wearing a snaffle and a dropped noseband	2
19	A grey Arab being ridden in a hackamore	6
20	A pony wearing a crupper	7
21	Someone plaiting a tail	6
22	A chestnut horse with four white socks	3

FIND THE LETTER

See if you can find the missing letters in these well-known equestrian phrases.

I frly dmt tht th bst f my fn I w t t hrs nd hnd

A hrs s wrth mr thn rchs

A hrs a hrs my kngdm fr a hrs

Th st n a hrs mks gntlmn f sm nd grms f thrs

N ft n hrs

Gpsy gld ds nt chnk nd glttr. t glms n th sn nd nghs n th drk

Th hrs s Gds gft t mnknd

f wshs wr hrss thn bggrs wld rde.

A cntr s a cr fr vry vl

A gd hrs s nvr a bd clr

Answers on page 29

TAKE YOUR PICK

Horse words can differ from country to country.
See if you can guess which is the correct meaning of the American words below.

1 Lead shank

(a) Horse with insensitive sides
(b) Lead horse in a pack train
(c) Lead rope
(d) Weight cloth

2 Floating

(a) Pulling a milk cart
(b) Horse's action which make you feel seasick
(c) Term used for a resistance when a horse loses balance on a corner
(d) Rasping a horse's teeth

3 Cowlick

(a) Special type of mineral fed to quarter horses
(b) Whorl
(c) Rope-burn caused by a lasso
(d) Whip

4 Buckskin

(a) Naughty horse
(b) Saddle-sore
(c) Dun-coloured horse
(d) Leather used for breaking tackle

5 Cooler

(a) Type of rug which keeps wet horses warm
(b) Isolation box with no windows
(c) Groom who walks racehorses after a race
(d) Specially made leg-shaped ice-packs

6 Throatlatch

(a) Windsucker strap
(b) Throatlash
(c) Door grid which prevents weaving
(d) Bird which commonly nests in Stables

7 Bell boot

(a) Equiboot
(b) Horse who always has one fence down
(c) Special cabinet where your trophies are kept
(d) Overreach boot

8 Pinto

(a) Horse with pigeon toes
(b) Premature foal
(c) Coloured horse
(d) Parasitic worm

Answers on page 29

QUICK THINKING

Under each heading below, see how many items you can list. For example, if the item was PONY BREEDS you could list Shetland, Connemara, Welsh Mountain, etc. Score one point for each item and make a time limit (e.g. 30 minutes). See who can win the most points in that time.

BEDDING	BITS	OFFICIAL PONY COLOURS	RUGS
WHIPS	SHOW JUMPS	POISONOUS PLANTS	BANDAGES
TROT	BOOTS	HORSE-FEED	SHOES
NOSEBANDS	HAY	SHAPES OF CLIP	SADDLES
WHITE MARKS ON FACE	BRUSHES	CROSS-COUNTRY FENCES	DRESSAGE MOVEMENTS

The Secret Ride

Here is a story about Jock and Ellie, who go on a surprise ride with their mother. Fill the gaps in the story with horsey words which have more than one meaning.

To make it easier, look at the list of words at the end of the story. If you don't know what a word means, you can find out by turning to the answer page.

Jock and Ellie were really excited. Today was the day of the Secret Ride. The two children had cleaned their tack and boots the night before, and their ponies Clogs and Sixpence were gleaming and ready for the adventure.

Ellie was a bit worried about riding along the road, but Jock reminded her that it was Mum's idea and that she would be coming too to look after them.

'Sixpence is good in traffic' he added, 'and you will be quite safe if you ride by the . . . .' I wouldn't worry. Most of the ride will be on . . . . . . paths anyway.'

It was a beautiful day. All the birds were chirping, but it was a plump brown . . . which sang the loudest song. The little ponies' hooves went . . . . clop down the lane – and apart from children's chatter, those were the only sounds which could be heard.

Soon they were on the . . . . . . path and Mum was able to point out the different crops, flowers and trees. But she didn't seem too impressed when they passed through a small paddock with hardly any grass to be seen. 'Look at all those thistles and . . . . ,' she said. 'That's a sure sign that the field has been overgrazed and is . . . . .'

They all enjoyed paddling in the stream, and the ponies had a drink. Ellie nearly fell off when a . . . . hopped on to a stone right in front of Sixpence and startled him.

Jock had to get off to spend a penny and was very pleased when he found a pheasant's . . . ., which he stuck in Clog's browband.

As they rode along, Ellie and Jock became more curious about the rucksack on Mum's back. They also wondered why Hollie, her horse, was wearing a rather colourful car . . . under her saddle. Every time they asked what they were for, Mum said 'Guess!'

Finally, they arrived in a little clearing in a large wood. There were lines of string tied to sturdy trees, so they were able to tie up the ponies safely with the headcollars and ropes that they had brought with them.

Mum lit a fire in a home-made barbecue which stood in the centre of the clearing. What a . . . . . she made! And out of the rucksack came sausages, fresh white . . . . filled with salad, crisps and all sorts of other goodies. It was a real feast. 'I wish you wouldn't . . . . your food, Ellie,' said Mum 'You'll have indigestion.'

After they had eaten, Mum sat against a huge horse . . . . tree and the children decided to explore. All was peaceful until a shriek rang out through the trees. Mum jumped to her feet and ran to find out what had happened. Jock had slipped into a huge, muddy puddle. He was . . . .; his clothes from his . . . upwards were soaking.

'What happened?' asked Mum.

'He had a . . . . . with danger!' squealed Ellie. 'I was an Indian and I crept up behind him. He had a shock and fell in!'

'She pushed me!' muttered Jock.

'I don't suppose I'll never find out what really happened', sighed Mum. 'Let's give you a hot . . . . . of tea and then we'll go home.'

Mum decided to take a short cut. They had to . . . . . around an old boundary . . . . then down a track which took them along the coast. Way below, they could see the sun setting over the . . ., and the white . . . . . . of the waves looked like sea horses.

By the time that they reached home, the first . . . . was twinkling in the sky. Jock had to . . . . . . a yawn. He didn't want anyone to know how tired he felt.

Dad came out of the house and as a special treat he helped Jock and Ellie to brush, water and feed their ponies.

After Sixpence, Clogs and Hollie were settled for the night, the family went indoors, tired and happy.

thrush · *cobs* · *frog*
curb · *chestnut* · *feather*
bridle · *bay* · *stifle*
docks · *star* · *wall*
brush · *socks* · *skirt*
blaze · *cup* · *stale*
bolt · *drenched* · *crests*
clip · *rug*

Answers on page 30

CRAFTY PAIRS

Jumbled up in the drawing are two other words which will fit on either side of each of the following. For example: Mealy NOSE and NOSE band. See how quickly you can match them up.

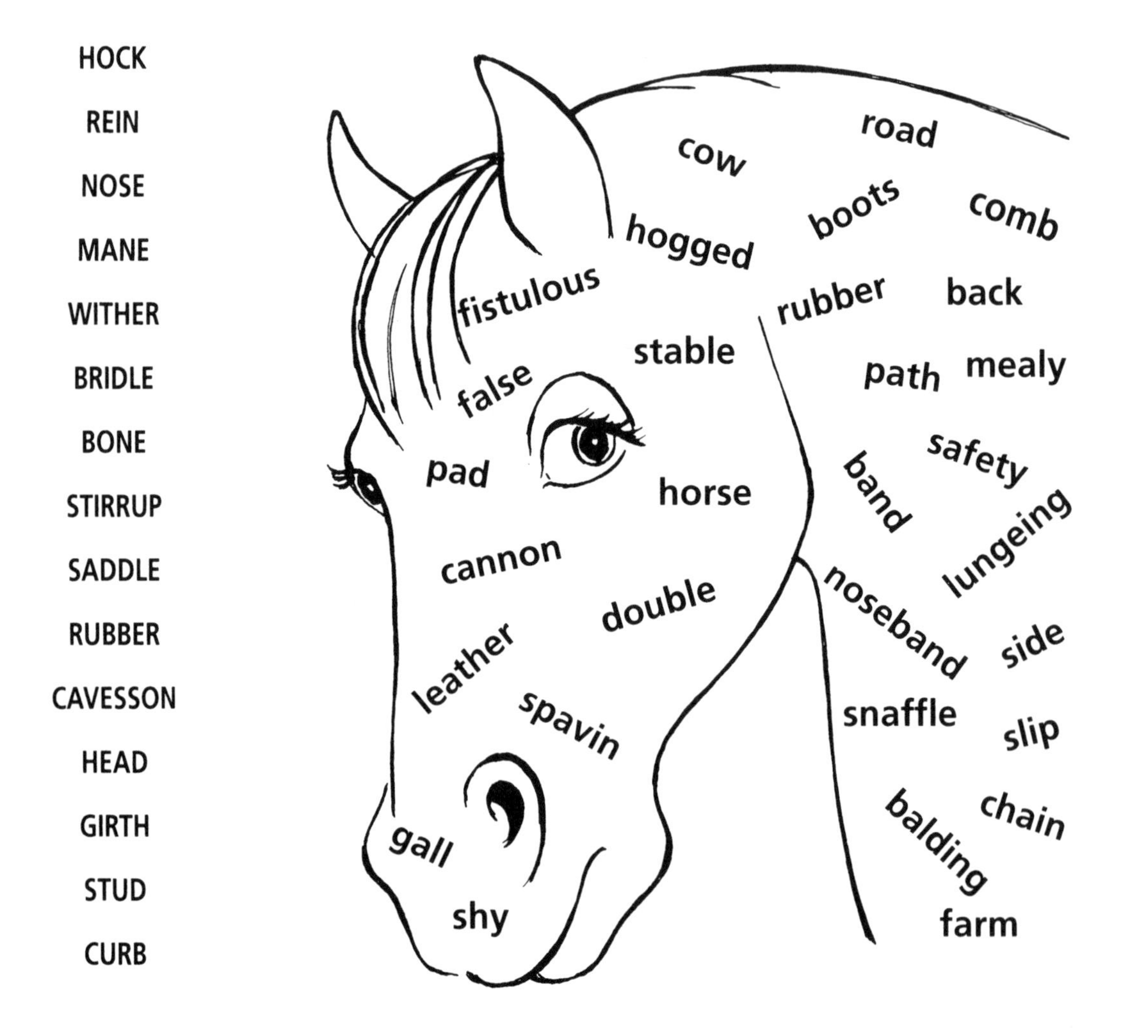

 Answers on page 30

WORDSEARCH

The words which you should look for are ponies' colours and markings. Most of them can be found on a horizontal or a vertical line, but three are on a diagonal.

Piebald	**Stripe**	**Brown**
Dun	**Stocking**	**Cream**
Chestnut	**Sock**	**Black**
Roan	**Skewbald**	**Blaze**
Star	**Bay**	**Palomino**
Snip	**Grey**	**Albino**

P A M N D C R E A M F N C G U E I S O C K N X B C V C H M S

I L K D N U I E F C H E S T N U T P I R F U D D Y W L K Y T

E K F S X M X P N F F S D M J J R A F H O K E W S X V N S A

B G H J K S D C B N S T R I P E Q L M N V A R U E J K N K R

A C V H G E E Z Q W R O C J K T Y O G D A Q N U Y T I S W R

L B J D G R W K P Z P C F H K I Y M N G S W H T Y P F B S G

D B G M K G F B L A C K E G H J K I B R O W N P S F J A D S

F H K L F H S F A Y I I H N V C S N G E M L X Z Q E Y Y C G

G S X D F V G B H L J N A L B I N O Y Y R E W X V F G B H Y

D U N M L S Q A Z E D G H W Y I P L M B H K T U R B L A Z E

CROSSWORD

ACROSS

1 Never ride without wearing one of these (3)
3 Dandy, Body and Water are all . . .? (7)
6 A metal comb for cleaning a body brush; or a hot food (5)
7 Scold a foxhound by using your voice (4)
8 A comfortable three-time pace (6)
11 Paint this on hooves for a finishing touch (3)
13 The undersides of saddles used to be made of this material (5)
14 What your pony does most when he is turned out (5)
16 If your pony does a lot of roadwork he needs to be . . .? (4)
17 An event in which cowboys ride bucking broncos (5)
18 More than two horses pulling a carriage (4)

DOWN

1 You need this to handle your pony when you are not riding him (10)
2 Saddles and bridles together (4)
3 The metal piece under the skirt of the saddle, over which the stirrup-leather lies (3)
4 Bigger than a pony (5)
5 Four bandages, four shoes, many showjumps or a badger's home (3)
8 Painful bruise sometimes caused by ill-fitting shoe (4)
9 Pony talk (5)
10 The top of the neck where much of the mane grows (5)
12 A pony whose training is complete (4)
15 Thrush is a sort of foot . . .? (3)

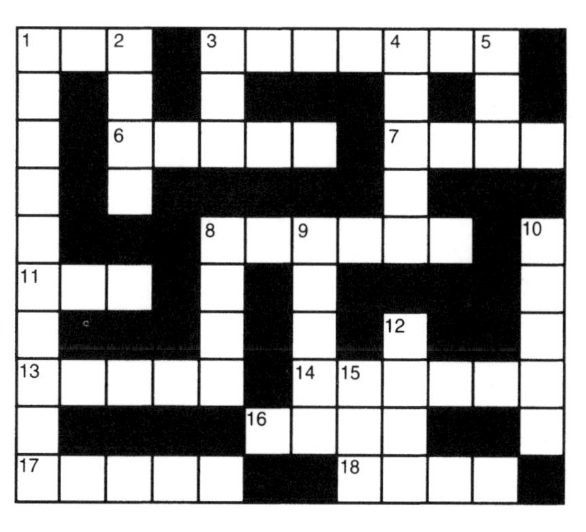

Answers on page 32

Fitting Question

Look at the objects. Do you know where they belong on a pony? See if you can name them and chose the correct statements.

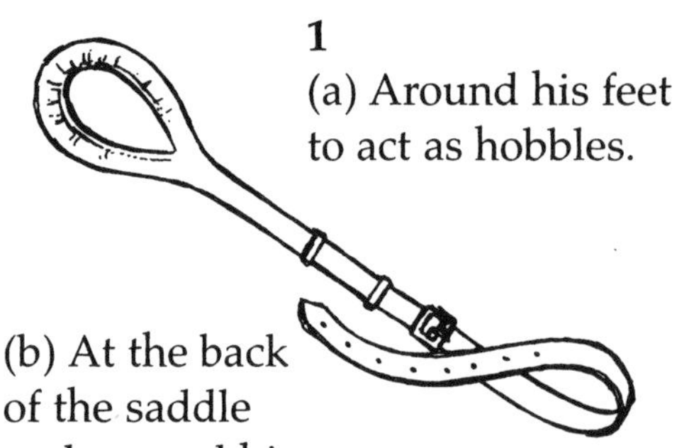

1
(a) Around his feet to act as hobbles.
(b) At the back of the saddle and around his tail to prevent the saddle slipping forward.
(c) Between his ears and around his nose to stop him running away.

2
(a) Over a nervous pony's ears, like ear-muffs.
(b) Around his tail to protect it when he is travelling.
(c) Over his feet to prevent injuries to his heels.

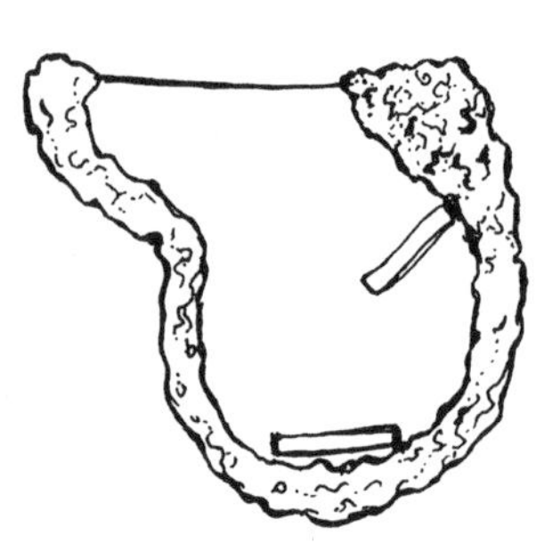

3
(a) Underneath the saddle to protect his back.
(b) Over a saddle to keep the rider warm.
(c) Under the girth to prevent rubbing

4
(a) Over a cart horse's eyes.
(b) Over his ears to protect his poll.
(c) Around his muzzle to prevent biting.

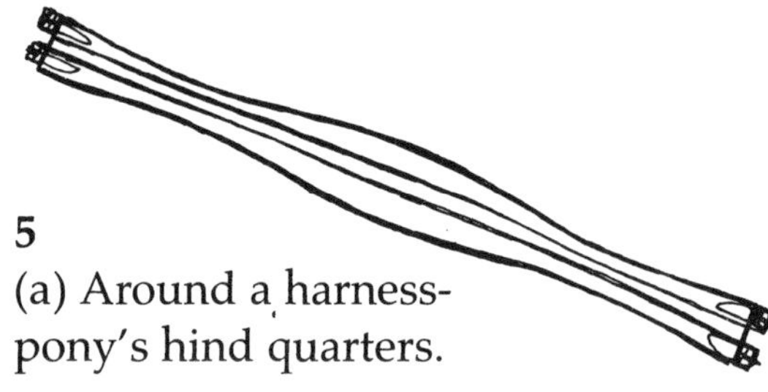

5
(a) Around a harness-pony's hind quarters.
(b) Under his belly, fastened to girth-straps on both sides of the saddle.
(c) Around his chest like a breast plate.

6
(a) On a cow's front foot.
(b) On a stable door
(c) On a pony's hind foot.

Answers on page 30

TRICKY TRAVEL

This pony is travelling to a show many miles away.
See how many faults you can find.

Answers on page 30

BAD TASTE?

Under each drawing is a circle. Tick if you think that the object is poisonous to ponies, cross if it is not

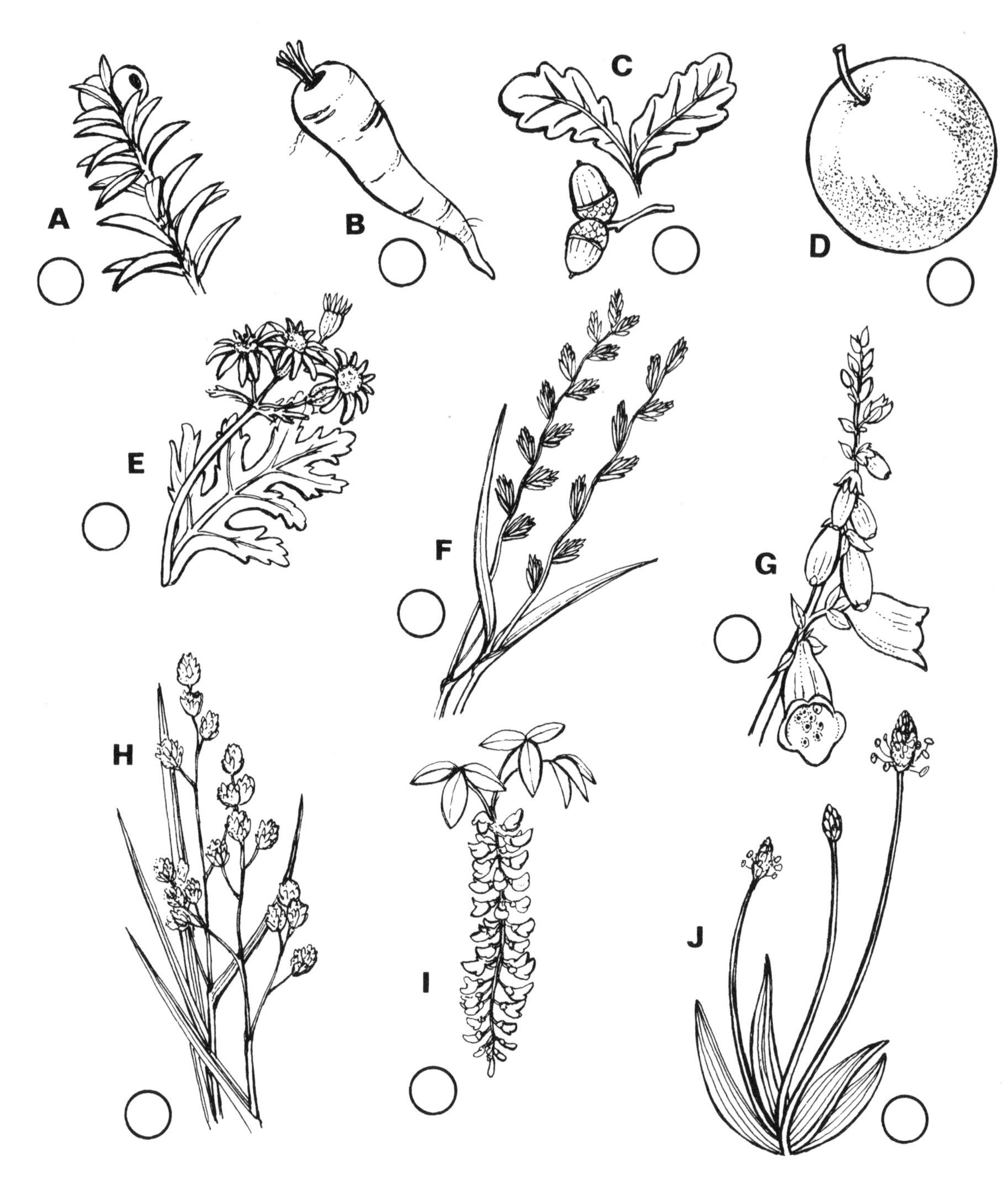

Answers on page 30

Search for Sindbad

Sindbad has bucked Jimmy off
and has cantered away through the woods.
Follow the woodland paths to help Jimmy catch his pony.

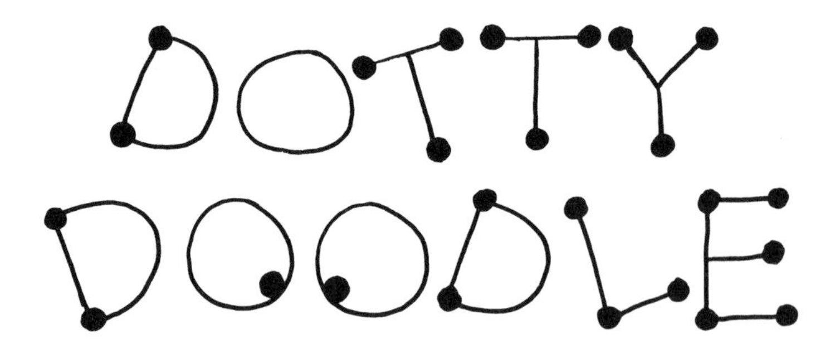

Join the dots to see who this mythological horse is.

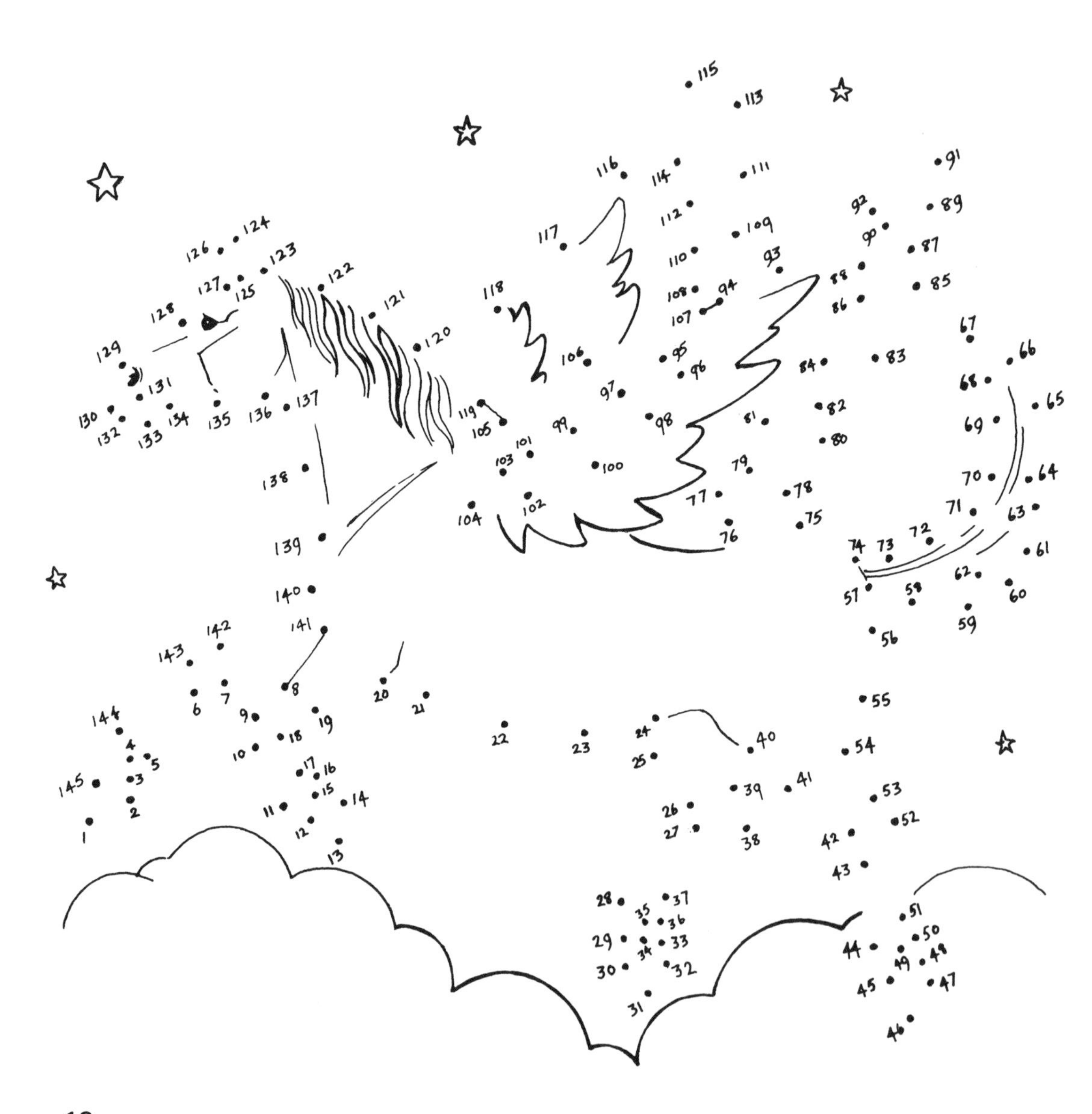

Just the Job

Decide which statement is true, and see if you can name the object.

1

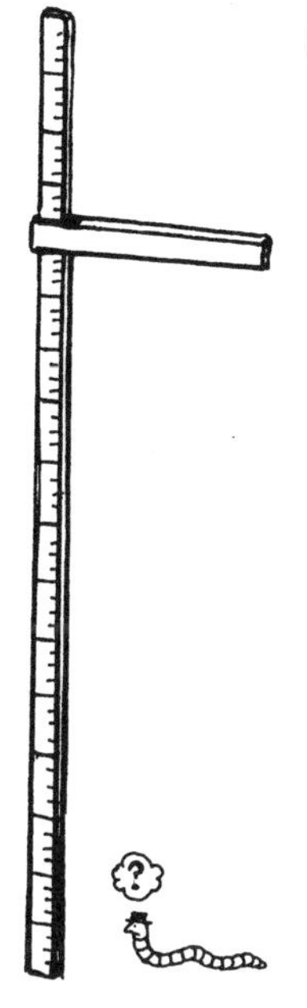

(a) It fits across the stable door in summer to keep a pony cool.
(b) It is a fold-away, travelling practice fence.
(c) It is used for measuring the height of a pony.

2

(a) It is a tool for making fancy patterns on show ponies' hind quarters.
(b) It is for cleaning the dust and grease from a body-brush.
(c) It is a mane-comb which works well on unruly manes.

3

(a) It is a band for plaiting manes.
(b) It fits on reins which are too long, and looks tidier than a knot.
(c) It is part of a stirrup.

4

(a) It fits across the top half of a stable door and can prevent weaving (bad behaviour).
(b) It fits around a pony's neck and stops him chewing his bandages.
(c) It is for teaching ponies how to jump over stiles and narrow places.

5

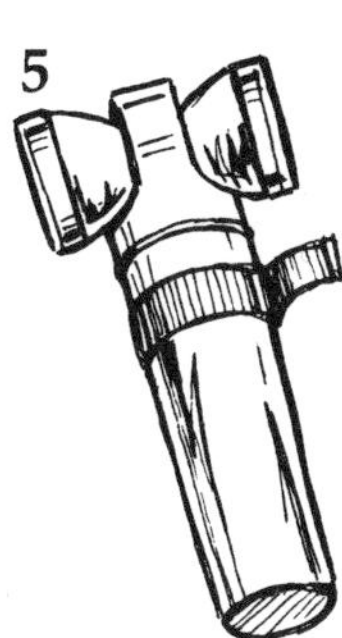

(a) A vet might use this for checking a pony's eyesight.
(b) It is a lamp which can be attached to a stirrup.
(c) It is a night-light for nervous ponies.

6

(a) It is outdoor shelter for rugs, bandages and grooming kit.
(b) It is a structure on which to iron rugs.
(c) It is something on which to store and clean saddles.

Answers on page 30

MIX AND

Match the riders' k

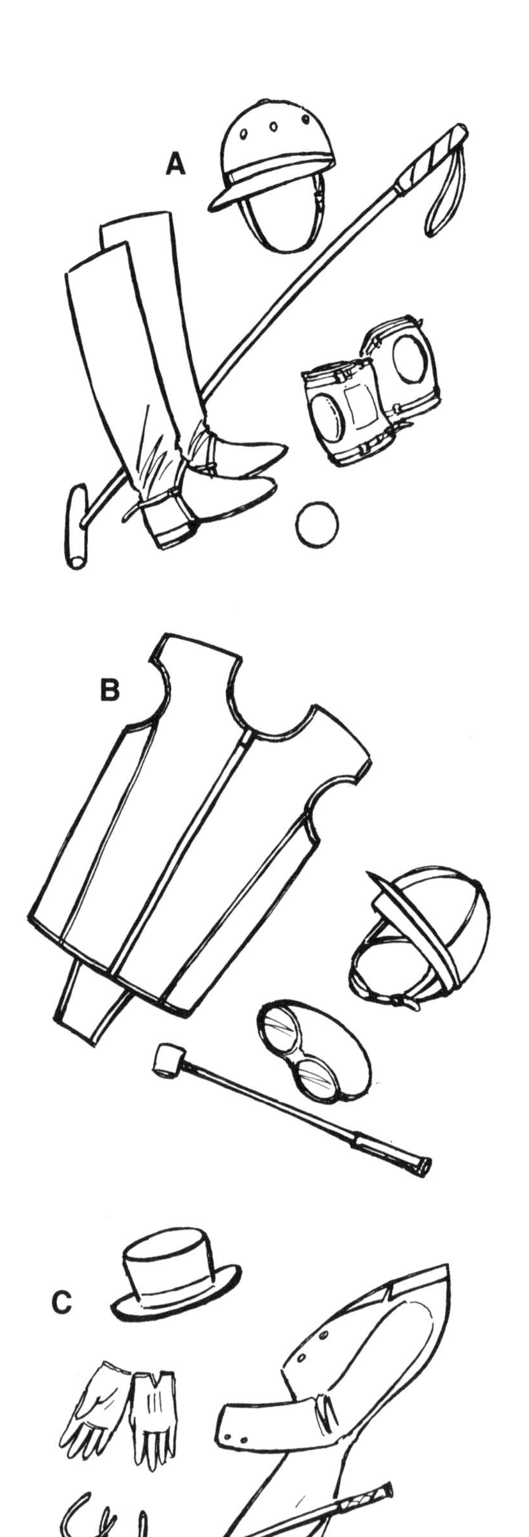

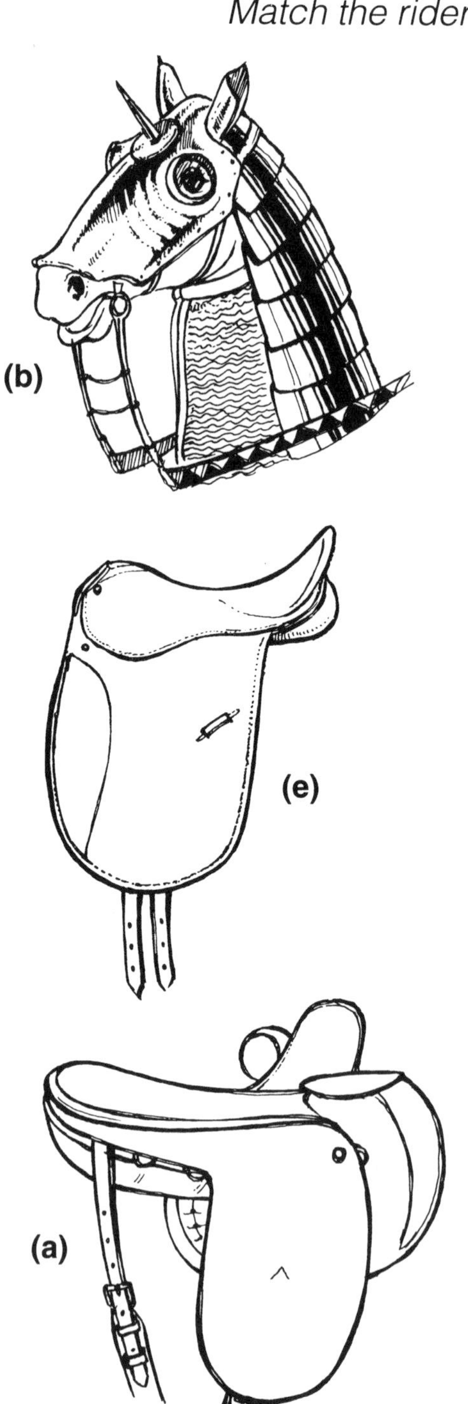

MATCH

ith the correct tack.

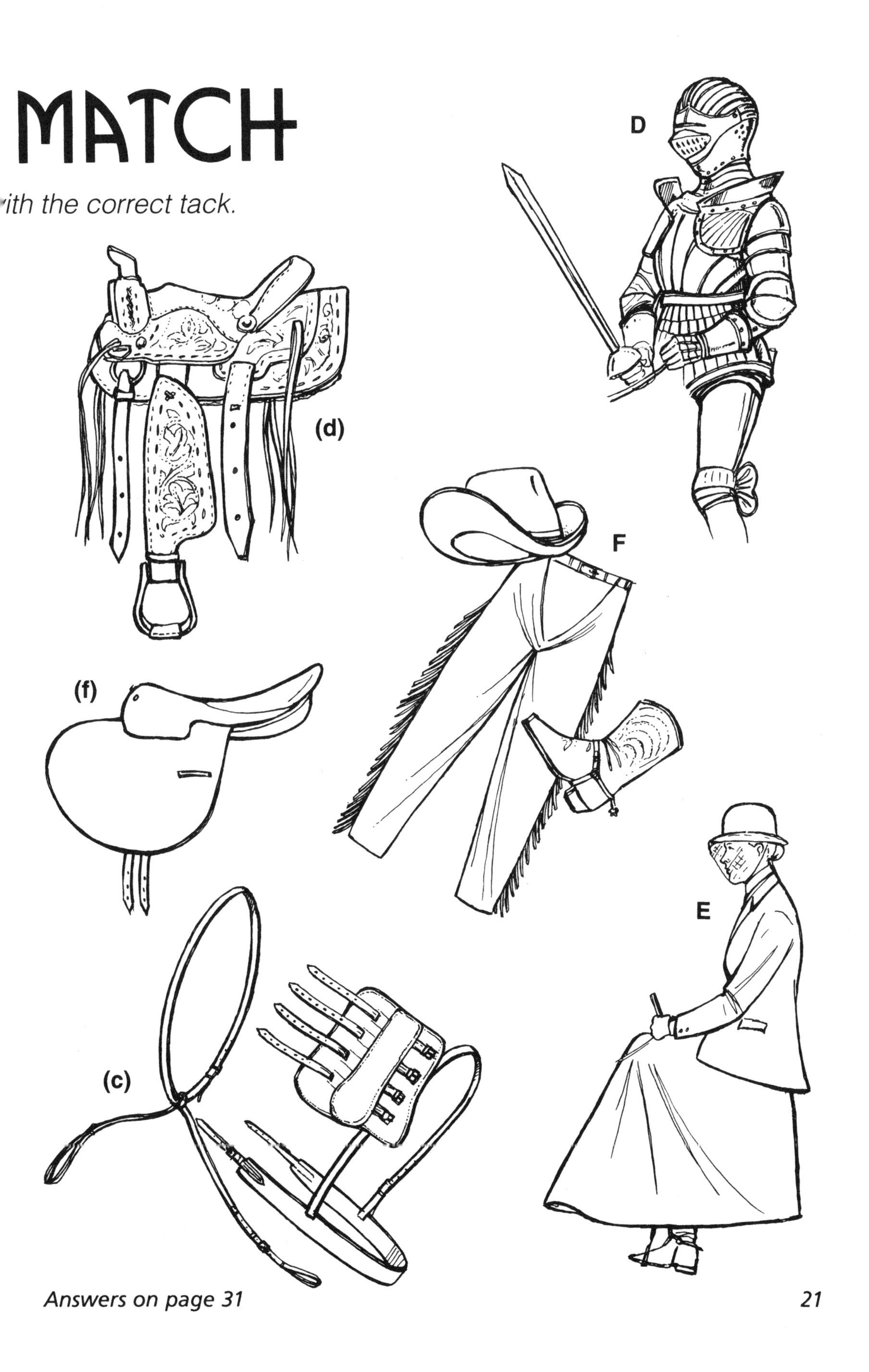

Answers on page 31

Katie-Jane Learns her Lesson

Part 2

Luckily, the washing-machine man had arrived and his van was parked just in the right place. Quick as a flash, Katie-Jane slipped the reins over the radio aerial and went inside. By now Wilbur was very cross. The day before had been a rainy one and he had spent a great deal of time and trouble rolling in a lovely muddy patch, so that he would have an extra layer to protect him against the cold. And now here he was, attached to a van in the baking sun, wishing he could roll the mud all off again. The other reason that Wilbur was not happy was that for several days he had had a stone stuck in his hoof and it was extremely uncomfortable.

Out came Katie-Jane. She slapped the saddle on to Wilbur's muddy back, then she sneakily led him out of the gate, across the road and into the next door field, which belonged to Farmer Hill.

Katie-Jane hadn't noticed that Farmer Hill's two hunters were grazing in the field with a herd of cattle. She was in so much of a hurry to ride that she had forgotten to shut the gate. She climbed up on to Wilbur and suddenly saw the cattle. "Wow, Wilbur!" she shouted, "Let's play cowboys on the range" and immediately galloped towards them.

Round and round they went, with Wilbur and the cattle getting hotter and hotter. To make matters worse, the hunters took fright, snorted like dragons, and flew their tails like banners in the air. They cantered amongst the cattle, with stiff legs and steps which made them look as though they were on pogo sticks. Then they became jealous and started to chase Wilbur, with their ears flat back and their teeth bared.

But worse was to come. The saddle started to slip and Wilbur could feel it slipping. He also knew that Katie-Jane was not wearing A HAT. He took off as fast as he could towards the muck heap which was in the corner of the field. He knew that it was bad enough to take a fall from a slipping saddle, but because Katie-Jane had nothing on her head, he needed a soft place for her to land before the saddle slipped any further. He reached the heap just in time, locked his knees and came to an emergency stop right in front of it. Katie-Jane flew over his head on to a deep bed of cow-muck and straw. Did it stink! It was so deep that she couldn't stand up in it, so she sat down and howled.

Wilbur turned and carefully (because the stirrups were now hanging under his belly by his feet) made his way to the gate. Just as he was going through on to the road, Farmer Hill drove up the lane in his Land Rover. He jumped out and caught the poor bewildered little pony.

Needless to say, Katie-Jane was in for a lot of trouble. But she never forgot the lessons she learned that day.

Answers on page 31

Barn Brain Bruiser

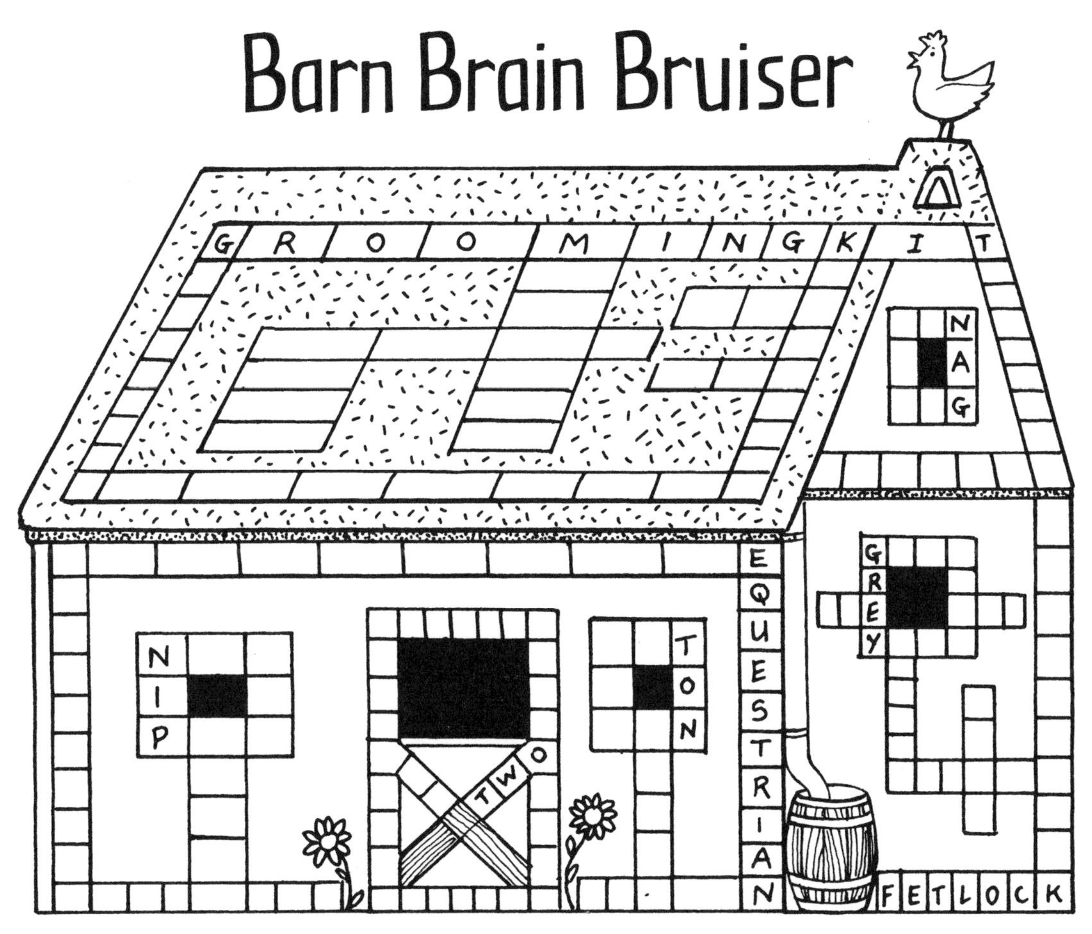

This is a criss-cross puzzle and once you have started, you will find it is not as difficult as it looks!

All you have to to is to fit the words listed below into the correct squares. New words begin with the first or last letter of the word before.

You will find that some of the words are already in position, to give you a head start.

Work in pencil, in case you make a mistake, and start with the long words first, as they will give you the key to the smaller ones.

WORDS WHICH FIT INTO THE ROOF OF THE BARN

Number of letters

11 Grooming kit

9 Grassland
Dartmoors
Tigertrap
Knee boots

7 Muscles
Stirrup

4 Dock
Dish

3 Toe
Cob
Run
Rug
Nag
Gag

WORDS WHICH FIT INTO THE FRONT OF THE STABLE AND THE STABLE DOOR

Number of letters

10 Side saddle
Equestrian
Shoulder in

9 Girth gall
Schooling

8 Near hind

7 Gallops
Landing

5 Apple
Irish
Green

3 Hay, Two, Bit,
Bar, Ran, Ton,
Nod, Pin, Nip
Dun

WORDS WHICH FIT INTO THE SIDE OF THE STABLE

Number of letters

10 Capped hock

7 Fetlock

6 Action
Numnah

4 Gait
Grey
Yard
Tied
Cane

3 Ice
End

Answers on page 31

Tigger's First Show

This is the story of what happened at Tigger's first show. Fill in the gaps with horsey words which have more than one meaning.

To make it easier, look at the words in the list below. If you don't know what a word means, you can find out by turning to the answer page.

dale
wisp
hand
cube
habit
Welsh Mountain
tree
groom
white line
lunged
skirt
heel
stocking
jewellery
table
mounted
roaring
double
Holstein
brand
whistling
broke out
bar
muzzle
stock
rubber rings
weaving

Tigger bounced as if he were on springs. This was not unusual. It was because he bounced that the family had called him "Tigger" after the character in Winnie the Pooh .

He was a short, long-legged , fuzzy-tailed foal. His mane stuck up as though he had had a fright, and today he was madly excited.

Clover, his dam, on the other . . . ., stood quietly with her ears up. Her beautiful bay coat shone like a polished . . . . .

Her mane was plaited, and not a . . . . of hair was out of place. The ramp was down and they were about to be loaded into the horsebox to go to a show.

"Don't worry, Tigger," said Jess, who was stroking him gently down his crest. "You do get in a flap! Clover will show you what to do."

Without any fuss, Clover climbed in, and Tigger, gently helped by all of the family, ... the ramp for the first time. He was soon inside and felt jolly proud of himself because everybody was telling him how good and brave he had been!

When they put the ramp up, Tigger wasn't sure that he liked being inside a dark . . . . . He looked nervously at Clover and was surprised to see that she hadn't even twitched an ear. She was busy tucking into a sweet-smelling haynet.

Bouncing was the last thing on Tigger's mind during the journey. The lorry was doing quite enough of that for both of them. To begin with, the . . . . of the engine and the . . . . of the wind rushing by were very alarming. But as the minutes passed, Tigger started to balance better, and soon he began to enjoy going up hill and down . . . . .

Finally they arrived. Clover wore a workmanlike . . . . . . bridle and Tigger had on a very smart foal slip.

As they came down the ramp, Tigger couldn't believe his eyes or his fluffy ears. What colours! What a noise! What an electric atmosphere! It was all too much for Tigger. Instead of bouncing as usual he . . . . . . into the air. It was all Jess could do to hold him. Then, Clover whickered to him, and he stood . . . . . still. Jess stroked and talked to him quietly, "Don't do that Tigger, it's a naughty . . . . . to get into."

After a while, Tigger had settled down enough to be shown the sights, and he saw some amazing things as they were in and out of the crowds.

First they went past the swings and the children's amusements. Tigger couldn't help but stop to watch children throwing . . . . around plastic ducks.

In the sheep-ring a red rosette had just been awarded to the best of the . . . . sheep, and as they passed the cattle ring a judge was looking for the best junior handler of . . . . calves.

Tigger was interested in everything. He was getter braver and braver. Even when he heard shouting and laughter coming from the . . . he didn't try to leap about, but walked on quietly behind his mother.

The children's ring was split into two, and at one end the fancy dress was in progress. The mare and foal stood to watch. Tigger felt really grown up because he was by the . . . which was to be the start and finish for the gymkhana events.

When the fancy dress was over, two children dressed as a bride and . . . . . came over to say "hello!"

Tigger was brave enough to sniff the bride's flowing white dress.

Finally they arrived at the hunter ring just in time to join the class for hunter broodmares with foals at foot. After

looking at all of the horses walking around, the judge decided to put Clover and Tigger in third place. But just as he was about to make his final decision, a terrible commotion . . . .

Into the ring came an enormous dog, wearing a . . . . . over his nose, followed by a lady wearing a mini . . . . ., ..., and lots of . . . . She was waving her arms and shouting at the dog to 'come to . . . .', but he took no notice and rushed towards the line of horses.

The first mare didn't like this . . . . . of behaviour. She stood up on her hind legs and galloped out of the ring followed by her foal and the owners. The foal in second position bucked with excitement and broke loose. His dam went 'bananas' and they also left the ring a great deal faster than they had entered it.

Tigger watched Clover carefully, so that he could copy her reactions. He didn't know that his mother had been a hunter and was used to large dogs. He saw that Clover was standing quietly. She lowered her nose to sniff the dog as he approached. The dog in turn stopped to sniff her, and as he did so he was caught by an official.

No one was surprised when Clover and Tigger won first prize, and the judge commented on Tigger's excellent manners.

The rosette tickled Tigger's face, but he could feel that it was something to be proud of, so he didn't shake it off. They slowly walked back to the horsebox for a drink and a bite of grass for Clover before the journey home. But after his drink, Tigger felt that there was no bounce left in him. He was so tired that he lay down under a large, shady oak . . . . and went fast asleep.

Jess and the family decided not to wake him up. After all, it had been a very long day for a foal. Clover munched grass happily and by the time the family had finished their picnic, Tigger was awake and ready for the journey home.

Answers on page 31

WORDSEARCH

In this wordsearch, look for items which you might find in a grooming kit. There are twelve in all. You will find them all on the vertical line, and three of them are upside down.

WISP
WATER BRUSH
CACTUS CLOTH
HOOF PICK

SWEAT SCRAPER
BODY BRUSH
HOOF OIL
SPONGES

STABLE RUBBER
DANDY BRUSH
MANE COMB
CURRY COMB

W S P J D S P F S K S J N D K U T K T M D O P L S D E R J F I

I K R N R W K B B R F G H J K D W R T J L Q W A G A H J K N M

S X F H J E L E O L J G D W Q Z A R U I K M C V R N E R Y J P

P D T H I A M F D S F H K P Y U T E W C B H F W Q D A D E H G

W R Y I P T S H Y F G J L S D C V N M W T Y D A C Y N M E S Q

E W Q C X S V M B F A Y I E D H G S W R T V B N Y B V Z A R J

C D F R S C G L R T D S O G J D G F T R B X Z K P R O O L M V

S F J W T R S I U J D E F Q T R S H S A G N B C V U F Y E W B

J F D S Q A Z X S F E O O L H D P H D S W C R Z G S H Y A L M

W D C F T P Y W H Q T U O N M D O T J W C D E J H H M F W Q O

A J A G E E T J G D S W H M B C N F R Q O P B H J F M N S R C

T L C T W R H G D S L O U Y T R G F E W T Y B I M B A W Z L Y

E Z T D G J O S F G K T E Y J D E J F D S A U R Y I N P L G R

R P U A Z C O N H F S W R T K E S F Q E T U R K H G E D S A R

B W S S E Q F E T B M S D G T L F A W V N Z E B M J C D R W U

R L C F G K P R I I D V N Y S H K L P U Y R L D Q R O O N C C

U A L M G J I D Q R T H J P K G D V C N B M B R H F M S F H D

S G O F J B C D J M S C T Y W A X Z N H J L A J G Y B J F G E

H H T F V N K Z Q W D S R G T H Y J U K I I T J F G D S H M V

A L H V R S K H D F V T B Y N I M P L M V B S Q A X Z B T J Q

Answers on page 32

I Say, I Say, I Say!
What did the colt say to the filly? Stop nagging me.
Why did the pony put up his umbrella? Because he saw the rein.
When is a pony like a chicken? When he pecks.
Why did the hound jog? Because he saw the foxtrot.
When is a pony like a coconut? When he shies.
What do you call a pony who likes to do the washing up? Dish face.
Why did the pony hack? Because he had the croup.
Why did he hackamore? Because he had the strangles.
When can a pony fly? When he has a pigeon toes, a parrot mouth, and feathers.
Why is it so difficult to reach a pony's brain? Because he has forelocks.
The Master: "Young man, your pony appears to be drunk!" Little Johnny: "Sorry Sir. It's the port!"
Why did the hunter 'ditch' his side-saddle rider? Because he didn't like the habit!
When is a pelham like Mr Spock? When it is vulcanite.

spot THE difference

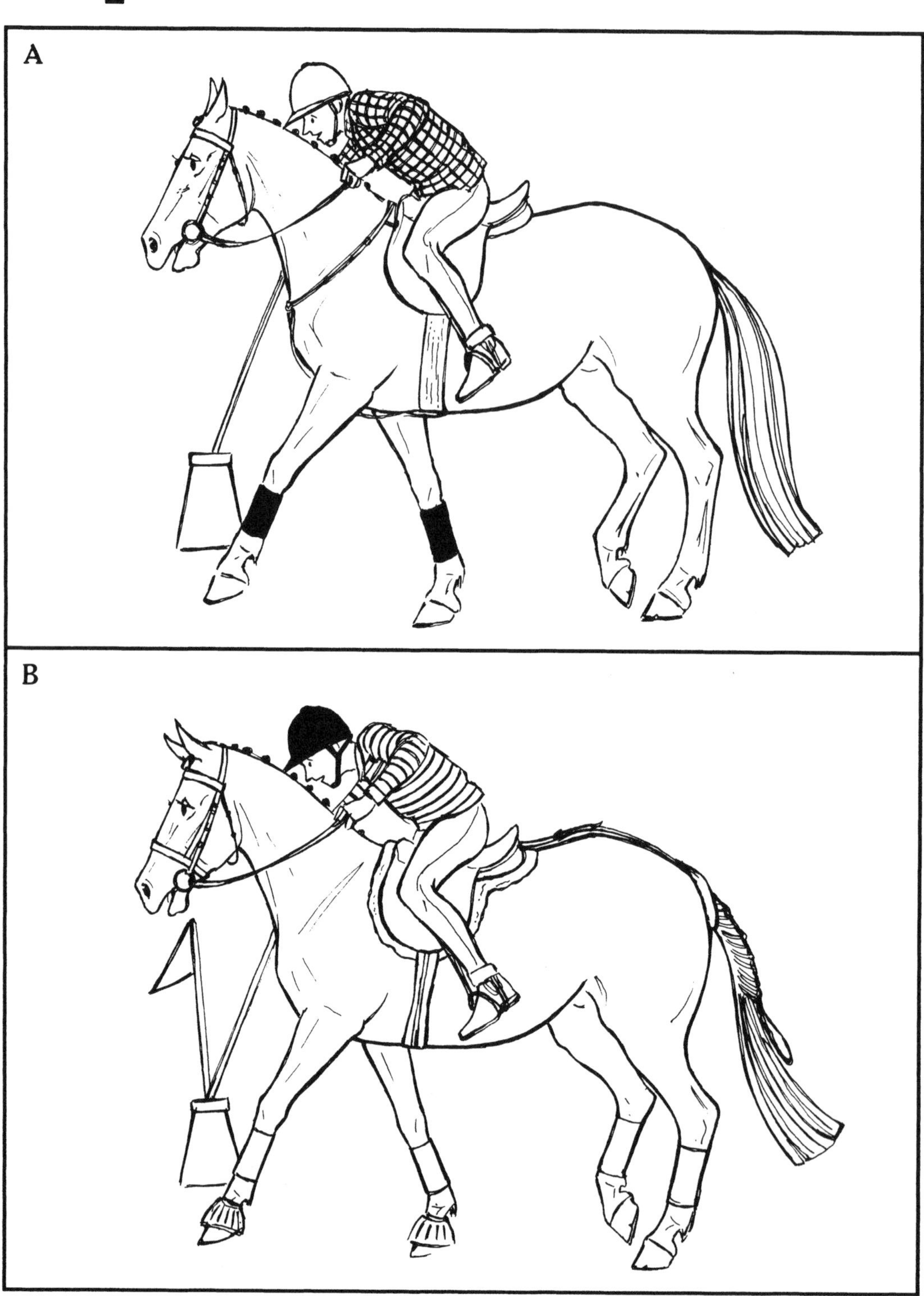

Answers on page 31

Answers

NAGAGRAM *page 1*

SHIRE	FELL	MORGAN
WELSH COB	DALE	ARAB
DARTMOOR	SHETLAND	QUARTER HORSE
NEW FOREST	EXMOOR	CASPIAN
CONNEMARA	PERCHERON	IRISH DRAUGHT

PONY POSERS *page 1*

1 (a) Piebald (b) Palomino.
2 A white mark between the nostrils.
3 Colts and fillies.
4 Pick out his feet.
5 Two sponges: one to clean eyes, nose and lips, the other to clean the dock area.
6 Untie him.
7 (a) String (nylon). (b) Tubular synthetic fabric (e.g. cottage craft). (c) Atherstone. (d) Balding. (e) Three-fold. (f) Webbing.
8 It prevents a saddle or roller from slipping forward.
9 (a) Tail bandage and/or guard. (b) Travelling boots or bandages. (c) Knee caps. (d) Hock boots. (e) Poll guard.
10 (a) Clean fresh water available at all times. (b) Feed little and often. (c) Feed according to work, temperament and condition. (d) Keep to the same feeding hours every day. (e) Don't work the pony hard straight after feeding. (f) Feed adequate roughage. (g) Introduce changes of food gradually. (h) Feed clean, good-quality forage. (i) Feed something succulent every day.
11 Privet, ragwort, foxglove, yew, laburnum, horsetail, hemlock, acorn, woody, black and deadly nightshade.
12 (a) The shoe is loose. (b) The clenches have risen. (c) The foot has become long and has grown over the shoe. (d) The shoe is thin. (e) The pony has lost a shoe.
13 A stud.
14 (a) 38°C (100.5°F). (b) 12 times per minute. (c) 36-45 beats per minute.

A BIT OF OF A PUZZLE *page 2*

(a) D-ring snaffle
(b) Rubber, straight-bar snaffle
(c) Fulmer snaffle (single-jointed snaffle with cheeks)
(d) Eggbut snaffle
(e) Hanging cheek snaffle
(f) Magenis roller snaffle
(g) Kimblewick
(h) Gag snaffle
(i) Curb bit
(j) Vulcanite pelham

CHARADES *page 4*

1 Browband (part of the bridle)
2 Appaloosa (an American horse or pony which has a spotted coat)
3 Cowlick (another word for a whorl)
4 Chestnut (a reddish colour)
5 Rubber curry comb (part of the grooming kit)
6 Dartmoor (one of the British native breeds of pony)
7 Piebald (a pony which has a black and white coat)
8 Forelock (the piece of mane which comes between the ears and over the pony's forehead)
9 Bareback (to ride without a saddle)
10 Highland (another native breed)
11 Coffin Bone (one of the three bones found in a pony's foot, sometimes called the pedal bone)
12 Stable (a building where horses and ponies are kept)

ACHES AND PAINS *page 5*

A / c B / e C / a D / b E / d

DEALER'S GAME *pages 6 and 7*

Ranger will suit Jerome 'Hotspur' Harkaway.
Iris will suit Madame Saccharin.
Hector will suit Jumbo Barleymow.
Primrose will suit Miss Willing.
Zanzibar will suit Ms Leatherbottom.
Golden Sovereign will suit The Hon. Mrs Fortescew-Ffitz-Blogs.

Cream Cracker should not be a novice showing "potential' at 11 years old! Being nervous in traffic is not a plus point.

Brainstorm is probably a difficult horse. You can read a lot into 'not a novice ride' or 'Never stops'. He is getting old and is not sold sound.

Cuthbert is gentle and uncomplicated. But he is very old and he is not sold sound.

FIND THE LETTER *page 8*

No foot no horse.
If wishes were horses then beggars would ride.
A good horse is never a bad colour.
A horse! A horse! My kingdom for a horse!
A canter is a cure for every evil.
A horse is worth more than riches.
The horse is God's gift to mankind.
Gipsy gold does not chink and glitter. It gleams in the sun and neighs in the dark.
The seat on a horse makes gentlemen of some and grooms of others.
I freely admit that the best of my fun I owe it to horse and hound.

Take your Pick *page 9*

1 (c) 2 (d) 3 (b) 4 (c)
5 (a) 6 (b) 7 (d) 8 (c)

THE SECRET RIDE *page 11*

Here are the words in the order in which they should be inserted, with explanations of their other (horsey) meanings.

curb	A thickening of the tendon on the hind leg, just below the point of the hock.
bridle	Leather head harness which secures the bit in a pony's mouth.
thrush	A disease of the foot which attacks the cleft of the frog. It is smelly.
clip	To shear off long winter coats with clippers.
bridle	See above.
docks	The boney part of ponies' tails.
stale	Horse or pony urine.
frog	V shaped, spongey underside of a pony's foot.
feather	Long hair which grows at the back of the fetlocks.
rug	Horse rug which keeps him warm in winter.
blaze	A long white mark down a pony's face.
cobs	Very strong, rather small horses.
bolt	To run away, out of the rider's control.
chestnut	A gingery-red colour.
drenched	When a pony has been given liquid medicine.
socks	White markings on a pony's legs.
brush	Either to groom a pony, or the item used for grooming.
cup	A metal fixture on a jump-stand, which holds up poles.
skirt	short flap on the saddle which covers the stirrup-bar.
wall	The insensitive outside shell of the hoof.
bay	A dark chocolatey, brown colour.
crest	The top of ponies' necks.
star	A small white mark between a pony's eyes.
stifle	A joint on a pony's hind leg.

CRAFTY PAIRS *page 12*

cow HOCK boots
rubber REIN back
mealy NOSE band
hogged MANE comb
fistulous WITHER pad
double BRIDLE path
cannon BONE spavin
safety STIRRUP leather
side SADDLE horse
stable RUBBER snaffle
lungeing CAVESSON noseband
slip HEAD shy
balding GIRTH gall
road STUD farm
false CURB chain

FITTING QUESTION *page 14*

1 (b) A crupper
2 (c) An overreach boot
3 (a) A numnah
4 (b) A poll guard
5 (b) An Atherstone girth
6 (c) A hind shoe

TRICKY TRAVEL *page 15*

Trailer

1 The trailer is not yet attached to a motor-car.
2 Its stabiliser legs are not down.
3 It has a flat tyre.
4 There is no partition.
5 There are no lights on the mudguards.
6 There are not enough slats on the ramp.
7 There are no clips to fasten back the top doors.

Handler

8 Not suitably dressed for leading a pony, especially the high-heeled boots and jewellery.

Pony

9 Is wearing a bridle with the rope attached to the noseband.
* Should be wearing a headcollar with a rope and possibly a poll-guard attached.
10 Is wearing a rug without anything to secure it.
* Should have a surcingle or roller over a wither pad; a tail-guard and a breast-girth could then be fitted.
11 Is wearing exercise bandages.
* Should be wearing travelling boots or bandages on all four legs.
12 Is wearing overreach boots on the hind feet.
* Overreach boots are normally fitted on the front.
13 Is not wearing a tail bandage.
* Should have a tail-bandage and possibly a tail-guard to save his tail from rubbing.
14 The rope from the pony's noseband is dangling on the ground.

BAD TASTE? *page 16*

A	Yew	✓	B	Carrot	✗	C	Acorns	✓
D	Apple	✗	E	Ragwort	✓	F	Rye Grass	✗
G	Foxglove	✓	H	Cocksfoot	✗	I	Laburnum	✓
J	Ribwort	✗						

JUST THE JOB *page 19*

1 (c) A measuring stick.
2 (b) A curry comb (not to be used on body or manes!).
3 (c) The rubber ring and leather attachment on a safety stirrup.
4 (a) An anti-weaving grille.
5 (b) A stirrup torch.
6 (c) A saddle horse.

MIX AND MATCH *pages 20 and 21*

A	(c)	Polo	D	(b)	Warrior
B	(f)	Racing	E	(a)	Sidesaddle
C	(e)	Dressage	F	(d)	Western

KATIE-JANE LEARNS HER LESSON
pages 3 and 22

Here are the things which you should have spotted.

Part One

1 You should never go riding without someone knowing (a) what you are doing, (b) where you are going and (c) how long you expect to be gone.

2 Shorts are uncomfortable and trainers are dangerous to ride in.
3 Katie-Jane should have taken a headcollar and rope, not a bridle, to catch Wilbur. She should also have taken some food.
4 Shouting does not please ponies.
5 Broken-down wire around a paddock is very dangerous for ponies.
6 Yew is poisonous to ponies.
7 Never sneak up on ponies, and never approach them from the rear, as you risk being kicked.
8 Old baths with taps are not ideal watering arrangements for ponies, who may injure themselves on them.
9 Katie-Jane did not put the bridle on correctly.

Part Two

10 Never tie your pony up by the reins.
11 Katie-Jane should have picked Wilbur's feet out every day.
12 You should brush the mud off before putting on the saddle, and the saddle should be put on gently.
13 If you open a closed gate, always shut it behind you.
14 Katie-Jane was not wearing a hat – which is very serious indeed.
15 She did not tighten the girths before mounting.
16 Ponies should be allowed to warm up before galloping.
17 Never chase farm animals.
18 Never ride in a field where there are unfamiliar loose horses. It can be dangerous enough riding in a field with horses whom you know.

BARN BRAIN BRUISER *page 23*

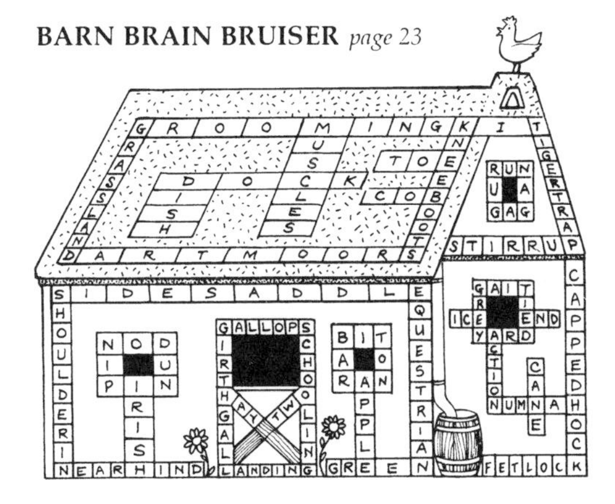

TIGGER'S FIRST SHOW *pages 24 and 25*

Here are the words in their horsey meanings in the order in which they should be inserted.

hand Ponies are measured in 'hands'. A hand is four inches.
table The part of a pony's tooth which grinds grass. The shape of the table changes as the pony gets older. Experts look at the tables to assess a pony's age.
wisp A massage-pad made out of a rope of twisted hay.
mounted To mount means to get on your pony.
cube Pony-cube is a feed which is a mixture of ingredients made into a nut.
roaring Some ponies have wind problems. Roaring is the noise they make when breathing in. It is especially noisy when they canter.
whistling The same as above, only the noise sounds higher and thinner.
Dale A British native breed of pony.
double Two fences with a related distance between them, counted as one obstacle.
lunged A pony who needs exercise but who cannot be ridden may be lunged in a circle around a person controlling him from the ground. This is done with a long lungeing rein, fixed to a lungeing cavesson on the pony's head.
stock Another word for a hunting tie which is folded neatly around the rider's neck and fastened with a stock-pin.
habit The matching coat and skirt worn by sidesaddle riders.
weaving a stable vice in which the horse sways from leg to leg.
rubber rings Ring-shaped boots which fit around the pastern of the hind leg. They help to prevent injuries caused by the opposite foot.
Welsh mountain A British native breed of pony.
Holstein A breed of carriage-horse; also a type of cow.
bar Part of a pony's mouth, an area in his foot, and the metal part of the saddle over which the stirrup-leather lies.
white line Part of a pony's foot.
groom To clean a pony with brushes or a person who looks after horses.
broke out When a pony breaks out, it means that he starts to sweat because he is under stress.
muzzle The end of a pony's nose.
skirt Part of the saddle.
stockings White or black markings which stretches up to the knee or hock on a pony's leg.
jewellery Old scars or injuries on a pony's legs.
heel Part of a pony's foot.
brand Some ponies are branded to denote ownership.
tree The skeleton around which a saddle is built.

SPOT THE DIFFERENCE *page 28*

Pony A	*Pony B*
No noseband	Noseband
Ears back	Ears forward
Wears a breast plate	Does not wear a breastplate
Has a string girth	Has a leather girth
One flag in the cone	Two flags in the cone
Dark bandages in front	Clear bandages all around
No overreach boots	Overreach boots
No numnah	Numnah
Tail unplaited	Tail plaited
No crupper	Crupper
Rider wearing clear hat cover and checked shirt	Rider wearing dark hat cover and striped shirt

CROSSWORD *page 13*

CROSSWORD *page 4*

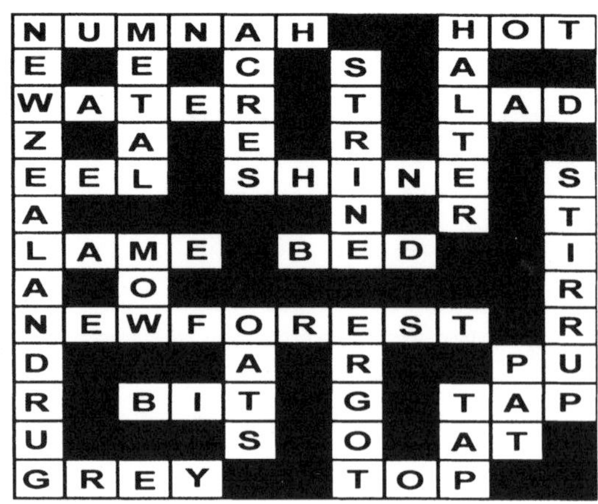

WORDSEARCH *page 13*

P A M N D C R E A M F N C G U E I S O C K N X B C V C H M S
I L K D N I E E F C H E S T N U T P I R F U D D Y W L K Y T
E K F S X X P P N F F S D M J J R A F H O K E W S X V N S A
B G H J K D C C B N S T R I P E Q L M N V A R U E J K N K R
A C V H G E Z Z Q W R O C J K T Y O G D A Q N U Y T I S W R
L B J D G W W K P Z P C F H K I Y M N G S W H T Y P F B S G
D B G M K F B B L A C K E G H J K I B R O W N P S F J A D S
F H K L F S F F A Y I I H N V C S N G E M L X Z Q E Y Y C G
G S X D F G B B H L J N A L B I N O Y Y R E W X V F G B H Y
D U N M L Q A A Z E D G H W Y I P L M B H K T U R B L A Z E

WORDSEARCH *page 26*

W S P J D S P F S K S J N D K U T K T M D O P L S D E R J F I
I K R N R W K B B R F G H J K D W R T J L Q W A G A H J K N M
S X F H J E L E O L J G D W Q Z A R U I K M C V R N E R Y J P
P D T H I A M F D S F H K P Y U T E W C B H F W Q D A D E H G
W R Y I P T S H Y F G J L S D C V N M W T Y D A C Y N M E S Q
E W Q C X S V M B F A Y I E D H G S W R T V B N Y B V Z A R J
C D F R S C G L R T D S O G J D G F T R B X Z K P R O O L M V
S F J W T R S I U J D E F Q T R S H S A G N B C V U F Y E W B
J F D S Q A Z X S F E O O L H D P H D S W C R Z G S H Y A L M
W D C F T P Y W H Q T U O N M D O T J W C D E J H H M F W Q O
A J A G E E T J G D S W H M B C N F R Q O P B H J F M N S R C
T L C T W R H G D S L O U Y T R G F E W T Y B I M B A W Z L Y
E Z T D G J O S F G K T E Y J D E J F D S A U R Y I N P L G R
R P U A Z C O N H F S W R T K E S F Q E T U R K H G E D S A R
B W S S E Q F E T B M S D G T L F A W V N Z E B M J C D R W U
R L C F G K P R I I D V N Y S H K L P U Y R L D Q R O O N C C
U A L M G J I D Q R T H J P K G D V C N B M B R H F M S F H D
S G O F J B C D J M S C T Y W A X Z N H J L A J G Y B J F G E
H H T F V N K Z Q W D S R G T H Y J U K I I T J F G D S H M V
A L H V R S K H D F V T B Y N I M P L M V B S Q A X Z B T J Q